2008

To
Lauren
Luv
Jim
Nanny Sue —

A Year of
POETRY

Illustrations by
Anne Grahame Johnstone

AWARD PUBLICATIONS LIMITED

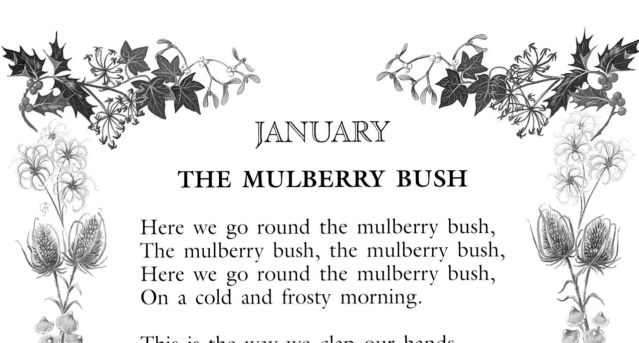

JANUARY

THE MULBERRY BUSH

Here we go round the mulberry bush,
The mulberry bush, the mulberry bush,
Here we go round the mulberry bush,
On a cold and frosty morning.

This is the way we clap our hands,
Clap our hands, clap our hands,
This is the way we clap our hands,
On a cold and frosty morning.

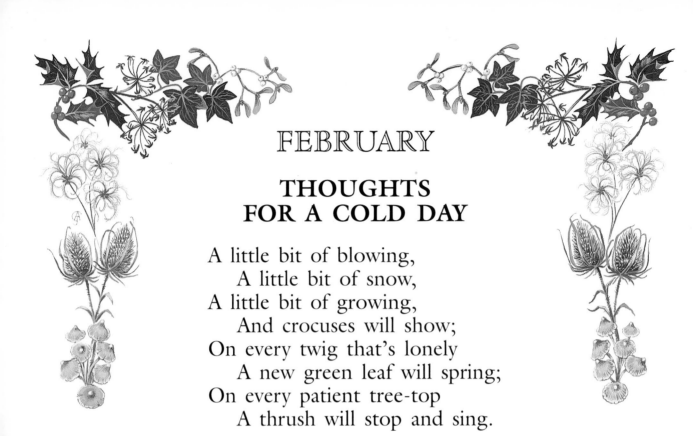

FEBRUARY

THOUGHTS
FOR A COLD DAY

A little bit of blowing,
    A little bit of snow,
A little bit of growing,
    And crocuses will show;
On every twig that's lonely
    A new green leaf will spring;
On every patient tree-top
    A thrush will stop and sing.

MARCH

A CHANGE IN THE YEAR

It is the first mild day of March:
　　Each minute sweeter than before,
The redbreast sings from the tall larch
　　That stands beside our door.

There is a blessing in the air,
　　Which seems a sense of joy to yield
To the bare trees, and mountains bare;
　　And grass in the green field.

William Wordsworth

APRIL

THUNDER

I hear thunder,
I hear thunder.
Hark! Don't you?
Hark! Don't you?
Pitter-patter, raindrops,
Pitter-patter, raindrops,
I'm wet through,
So are you.

MAY

I LOVE LITTLE PUSSY

I love little pussy,
    her coat is so warm;
And if I don't hurt her,
    she'll do me no harm.
So I'll not pull her tail,
    nor drive her away,
But pussy and I
    very gently will play.
She shall sit by my side,
    and I'll give her some food;
And she'll love me because
    I am gentle and good.

I'll pat pretty pussy,
    and then she will purr;
And thus show her thanks
    for my kindness to her.
But I'll not pinch her ears,
    nor tread on her paw,
Lest I should provoke her
    to use her sharp claw.
I never will vex her,
    nor make her displeased –
For pussy don't like to be
    worried and teased.

JUNE

THE FLOWERS

All the names I know from nurse:
Gardener's garters, Shepherd's purse,
Batchelor's buttons, Lady's smock,
And the Lady Hollyhock.

Fairy places, fairy things,
Fairy woods where the wild bee wings,
Tiny trees for tiny dames –
These must all be fairy names.

Robert Louis Stevenson

JULY

HARVEST SONG

The boughs do shake
   and the bells do ring,
So merrily comes our harvest in,
Our harvest in, our harvest in,
So merrily comes our harvest in.

We have ploughed, we have sowed,
We have reaped, we have mowed,
We have brought home every load,
Hip, hip, hip, harvest home!

AUGUST

LAVENDER'S BLUE

Lavender's blue, dilly, dilly,
Lavender's green;
When I am king, dilly, dilly,
You shall be queen.

Call up your men, dilly, dilly,
Set them to work,
Some to the plough, dilly, dilly,
Some to the cart.

Some to make hay, dilly, dilly,
Some to thresh corn,
Whilst you and I, dilly, dilly,
Keep ourselves warm.

SEPTEMBER

GIRLS AND BOYS

Girls and boys, come out to play;
The moon doth shine as bright as day.
Leave your supper and leave your sleep,
And join your playfellows in the street.

Come with a whoop
    and come with a call,
Come with a good will or not at all.
Up the ladder and down the wall,
A half-penny loaf will serve us all.

You will find milk and I'll find flour,
And we'll have a pudding
    in half an hour.
Come, let us dance on the open green,
And she who holds longest
    shall be our queen.

OCTOBER

WHO HAS SEEN THE WIND

Who has seen the wind?
Neither I nor you:
But when the leaves hang trembling
The wind is passing through.

Who has seen the wind?
Neither you nor I:
But when the trees
   bow down their heads
The wind is passing by.

Christina Rossetti

NOVEMBER

WOOD FOR BURNING

Beechwood fires burn bright and clear
If the logs are kept a year;
Chestnut's only good they say
If for years 'tis stored away;
Birch and firwood burn too fast,
Blaze too bright and do not last;
But ashwood, green and ashwood brown
Are fit for a queen with a golden crown.

Oaken logs if dry and old
Keep away the winter's cold;
Poplar gives a bitter smoke,
Fills your eyes and makes you choke;
Elmwood burns like churchyard mould,
Even the very flames are cold;
Applewood will scent the room,
Pearwood smells like flowers in bloom;
But ashwood wet and ashwood dry,
A king may warm his slippers by.

DECEMBER

THE HOLLY'S UP

The holly's up, the house is all bright,
The tree is ready, the candles alight:
Rejoice and be glad, all children tonight!

The mother sings of
    our Lord's good grace
Whereby the Child who saved our race
Was born and adored in a lowly place.

Once more the shepherds, as she sings,
Bend low, and angels touch their strings:
With 'Glory' they hail
    the King of kings.

The children listening round the tree
Can hear the heavenly minstrelsy
The manger's marvel they can see.

Let every house be ready tonight –
The children gathered,
    the candles alight –
That music to hear, to see that sight.

ISBN 0-86163-870-0

This edition first published 1997
by Award Publications Limited,
27 Longford Street, London NW1 3DZ

Printed in Belgium